YOU ARE ABOUT

LIKE, MAD

. . . especially if you haven't paid for this book, and you want to finish it before the man spots you!

SO HERE ARE A FEW THINGS YOU SHOULD KNOW . . . in case you want to change your mind!

LIKE, MAD
    . . . IS NOT "SQUARE!"
It's much longer than it is wide!

LIKE, MAD
    . . . IS REAL "COOL!"
If you keep it in the refrigerator!

LIKE, MAD
    . . . IS "THE MOST!"
The most asinine stuff you've read!

LIKE, MAD
    . . . IS "THE END!"

The end of a long line of successful paperback books if it doesn't sell . . .

LIKE, MAD

More **MAD** Humor from SIGNET

WILLIAM M. GAINES'S

LIKE,

Albert B. Feldstein, Editor

A SIGNET BOOK from
NEW AMERICAN LIBRARY
TIMES MIRROR
New York and Scarborough, Ontario
The New English Library Limited, London

SIGNET TRADEMARK REG. U.S. PAT. OFF. AND FOREIGN COUNTRIES
REGISTERED TRADEMARK—MARCA REGISTRADA
HECHO EN CHICAGO, U.S.A.

SIGNET, SIGNET CLASSICS, SIGNETTE, MENTOR AND PLUME BOOKS
are published *in the United States* by
The New American Library, Inc.,
1301 Avenue of the Americas, New York, New York 10019,
in Canada by The New American Library of Canada Limited,
81 Mack Avenue, Scarborough, 704, Ontario,
in the United Kingdom by The New English Library Limited,
Barnard's Inn, Holborn, London, E.C. 1, England

PRINTED IN THE UNITED STATES OF AMERICA

CONTENTS

The other day, we stopped in at our local "art" theater to see a double bill of foreign films . . . you know, those imports that are supposed to be free of censorship . . . and we made a startling discovery. *They're a fraud!* The first picture was in French, and since we hadn't paid much attention back in High School when we were supposed to be learning the language, we were forced to read the English titles that flashed on the screen. We were following the goings-on pretty well this way, when we happened to notice that the guy with the beret and the pencil-striped moustache on our right was laughing uproariously at parts we didn't think were particularly funny, and snickering knowingly at parts we didn't think were particularly sexy. And the same thing happened to the guy with the handle bar moustache eating the hero sandwich on our left when the Italian picture came on. So it suddenly occurred to us that them English titles don't quite tell *all* that's going on! The way we figure is . . . . . SOMEBODY'S COVERING UP! Study the following typical scenes we noted, and see if you don't agree that . . .

The English titles

the

FOR

MO

don't quite match

action in

EIGN

VIES

THE RESTAURANT SCENE

THE JEWEL ROBBERY

We will be caught for certain, you know, Jock . . .

It is only a matter of time, you know, Jock . . .

I know, Henri. Crime does not pay!

THE SHIPPING OUT SCENE

Joe! Tell me it isn't true, Joe!

Tell me you're not leaving, Joe!

Not without keeping your promise to me, Joe!

You can't leave, Joe.
Not like this . . .

Joe! What about my baby, Joe?

You promised you'd give my
baby chewing gum, Joe!

THE STREET SCENE

Hello, Lucille . . .

I've been waiting two hours, Sidney. You're late!

Mother is sick! She's asking for you!

END

LEAD PAN ALLEY DEPT.

We figure, if they keep testing H-bombs, there'll be some changes made over the next few years. Take f'rinstance popular music. Popular music is bound to reflect these changes. So here's our idea of the kind of songs young lovers of future generations will be singing as they walk down moonlit lanes arm in arm in arm in arm..

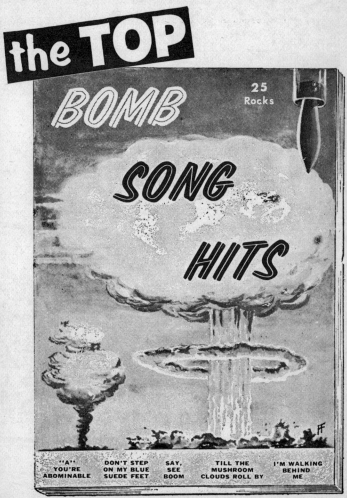

the TOP

25 Rocks

BOMB SONG HITS

| "A" YOU'RE ABOMINABLE | DON'T STEP ON MY BLUE SUEDE FEET | SAY, SEE BOOM | TILL THE MUSHROOM CLOUDS ROLL BY | I'M WALKING BEHIND ME |

The following are the top song hits of America, as determined by a recent nation-wide survey of all juke boxes, disc jockeys, and name bands located in caves around the country.

YOU'RE LOATHSOME TO LOOK AT

JONNIE OSSZEFOGVA

You're lovely to look at,
Delightful to know,
And *forty feet* high.
Because you're up in the sky,
I think the most impossible thing to do
Is walk down a lane holding hands with
     you.
You're lovely to look at,
Delightful to know
But this cannot last.
'Cause when I try to kiss you good-night,
I get nauseous from all that height,
     my dear.

THERE'S NO STREET
WHERE YOU LIVE

SAMMY AXOLOTL
OZGOOD Z'BEARD

I have often walked
    On this street before,
But there once was pavement
    Underneath my feet before.
Now as I walk by,
    I see rubble fly,
Boy, it's *rough* on the street
    Where you live!

People stop and stare,
    They don't bother me!
Got lead underwear,
    I'm safe as safe can be!
All the air is filled
    With radioactivity.
And it's *worse* on the street
    Where you live!

Oh, that frightening feeling
As the glow spreads over the land.
That exposed-to-lightning feeling
When those geiger counters click
    to beat the band!

There are no more trees,
    They've been all knocked down.
You will never hear a bird
    In any part of town.
See the plane draw near!
    Let's get out of here!
Yucca Flats is no street
    Where to live!

THE THING THAT
I MARRY

WHAT-ME NEUMAN
ALFRED E. WORRY

The girl that I marry
    Will have to be
A purple-skinned beauty
    With two heads or three.

The girl I call my wife
    Will have a nose
With eight nostrils
    You play like a fife.

Her nails will be claw-like,
    And in her hair
She'll wear geiger-counters,
    And I'll be there

'Stead of flyin', I'll be sighin'
    Next to her,
And she'll roar like a lion.
    The girl I propose to
Will have fourteen toes too,
    Like me!

SPACE SHIP

SCHROEDER
"BEE" THOVEN

Space ship,
Space ship,
Go so fast!
Space ship,
Space ship,
Shoot right past!
Earth is no more place to stop!
Since H-Bomb make it pop!

MAMA, LOOK-A H-BOMB

MELVIN COWZNOFSKI

Mama, look-a H-Bomb,
    They shout,
Their mother tell them,
        Watch for fallout!
Look-a your Daddy,
        He know!
Was fallout make him ugly so!

Hit the dirt!
        Join the crowd!
Mama look-a mushroom cloud!
            (*repeat*)

MY BLUE SHELTER

IRVING POTRZEBIE

Whenever I hear
    A bomb test is near,
I hurry to
    My Blue Shelter.

A hole in the floor,
    A six-inch lead door,
Will lead you to
    My Blue Shelter.

You'll see a smiling face
    Without a trace
Of coming doom.
    A little nest
That's nestled where
    The H-Bombs boom.
Just Molly and me,
    Let's see, that makes three!
We're happy in
    My Blue Shelter.

END

MAD

COATS

OF

ARMS

In the Middle Ages, when you got rich and famous because you could swing a sword faster and better'n the next guy, you got yourself a coat of arms. Every symbol in your coat of arms meant something. Your coat of arms told all about *you* . . . whether you were cowardly or brave, weak or strong, ignorant or stupid. Below the coat of arms was your family motto, usually in Latin so nobody would catch wise. Most coats of arms hung on the walls of old castles, above old fireplaces, next to old broadswords, old paintings and old enemies. Today, hardly anybody who gets rich and famous gets themselves a coat of arms. And today, just because hardly anybody does it swinging a sword is no excuse. So we offer some rich and famous people these coats of arms, free, from Mad.

Liberace

DIMPLUS NAUSEUM

Betty Furness

AUTOMATICA DEFROSTI

Jack Webb

DOM - DA - DOM - DOM

Elvis Presley

IN HOC HOUNDOG

Greta Garbo

I vant ta be alone!

Marilyn Monroe

Norman Rockwell

END

A SCENE WE'D LIKE TO SEE

The Fighter

1

2

3

4

28

5

6

7

8

9

10

"Alice is here, and your mother forgives you!"

11

Interlandi

12

END

SEEING IS BELIEVING

You've heard about this "Picture-Phone"... the coming telephone system where you not only hear, but see the person you're talking to? Well, we at MAD are worried about a big problem its use is sure to create. And we're not talking about the problem: How you gonna answer the "Picture-Phone" when it rings while you're taking a bath? This is no problem for us, since we don't take baths. What we're worried

MAD PICTURE-BACK

FOOL YOUR BOSS...

about is the problem: How you gonna tell them little white lies, when the people you're trying to fool can see for themselves you're a faker? The solution, as we see it, is: Some smart operators . . . Us, for example! . . . should bring out a kit specifically designed for fooling people on "Picture-Phone". You would merely tell them little white lies while standing before old window shades cleverly converted into:

'S
-PHONE
DROPS

FOOL YOUR WIFE...

END

And now, MAD, mindful of its responsibility to readers and anxious to allow them to

MOTOR

BE

(The cops

gain any advantage, however small, over
non-readers, presents this next vital article.

IST

WARE !

are on your tail)

First strategic move came when police deduced
that isolated two-tone patrol cars were easily
recognized by motorists driving all black cars.

Strategic move by police consisted of painting
two-tone patrol cars black to match motorists'
black cars, thereby forestalling recognition.

WAR OF RECOGNITION

Motorists retaliated quickly by trading in black cars for pastel-colored varieties, thus again isolating rare, out-of-place black patrol cars.

Police Departments around the country are going all-out to enforce the laws of the highways, and rightly so. Yes, even MAD is for highway safety and law enforcement. But it is the method used that we object to . . . method being this trend toward non-police-looking police cars that catch the unsuspecting motorist unawares. Up to now, motorists have been able to cope with the problem of how to recognize police cars (see above), despite the Police Departments' insidious campaign to remain hidden. But recently, MAD learned that the latest move on the part of the motorists (taking to wearing bright hued clothing) has infuriated the Police Departments. After all, an officer of the law must wear a uniform, or else how are people going to respect him? So now, the police have come up with the most devilish

(cont.)

BETWEEN MOTORISTS

Police counterattacked by discarding rare black patrol cars, acquiring new pastel-colored ones to match motorists', again gaining advantage.

plan of all to trap the motorist into the traffic courts. Disguised patrol cars that don't even look like *cars!*

The indignant editors of MAD feel that fire should be met with fire. After exhaustive research we have spied out the majority of disguises planned and are herewith exposing them. We are also preparing a booklet entitled, "How to Disguise Your Car and Thus Avoid Inconvenience."

This booklet will tell how, with a little paint and some minor revisions, you can make your car appear like a small ranch house, a rock garden or a base fiddle. If you wish to obtain this booklet, simply address a card "To whom it may concern" and deposit it in the pouch of any large kangaroo you see at the zoo. We feel that, for the time being, it's best to keep this movement as well-hidden as possible.

AND POLICE TO DATE

Motorists' latest move was to adapt outlandish clothing styles like plaid caps and chartreuse jackets, thus isolating dull police uniforms.

But war of recognition is not yet over. While motorists drive on with a false sense of security, police are readying secret weapons

GOOD HUMOR TRUCK

Police mobile radar unit disguised as a Good Humor truck will check speeding cars. Alert motorists, however, will be able to tell fake police Good Humor truck from real thing. Police Good Humor man will be too busy consulting radar screen to ring his bell. If you see a Good Humor man who is not ringing his bell . . . slow down!

WEAPONS...DISGUISED POLICE CARS

LEMONADE STAND

Police helicopter disguised as lemonade stand will hover over highways and trap speeders. However, alert motorists will be able to tell fake police stand from real one. Real lemonade stand will not have rotating umbrella and, depending on strength of lemonade sold, real stand will not be more than a foot off the ground. Careful!

FOUR-MAN BOBSLED

BABY CARRIAGE

Innocent-looking baby carriage will be another device to catch erring motorists. Carriage, equipped with 180 horsepower engine, will do 85 mph, accelerating to top speed from a standing start in 12 seconds. Carries one midget policeman inside, regular-sized policeman as steerer. Watch for steerer's retractable roller skates!

Keep an eye out for this baby on hilly highways. Disguised as a four-man bobsled, this device is powered by a 225 hp. engine with a 9.25 to 1 compression ratio and four-speed transmission. It carries two policemen, a recording clerk and a traffic court justice for on-the-spot trials. Watch for tell-tale gavel-rapping anchor man!

SLED AND DOG TEAM

By this winter, police will have put into action patrol unit disguised as Alaskan sled complete with 8 mechanized huskies. A V-1 motor will be concealed in each of the mechanical dogs, giving this job the equivalent of a V-8 dogpower engine. To tell fake police sled and dog team from the real thing on icy roads . . . listen for barking! **END**

NANSY

Recently, while scanning the pages of our favorite newspaper in search of material to swipe, our attention was magnetically drawn to the above comic strip. In fact, every day our attention is magnetically drawn to this comic strip because it always has a simple unique style, because it always has a simple unique gag, and mainly be

by Ernie Brushfiller

cause we've always had a uniquely simple mind. After we read it (and hated ourself for our weakness), we thought about the unique style of this comic strip and how the same strip would look in the unique styles of other comic strips. Here, then, is MAD's version of how those other comic strip's artists would interpret Ernie Brushfiller's . . .

NANSY DUCK

DICK NANSY

LI'L NANSY

ABNER MAE!! YO SHOULD BE ASHAMED OF YOSEF!!

A GOOD CLEAN-LIVIN' AMERICAN MOUNTAIN BOY SMOKIN' A *CEEGAR*...

NANSY CANYON

HI, GORGEOUS! GOT A HOT LIGHT FOR A COLD CIGAR?

SURE, HANDSOME ...I GOT EVERYTHING!

BUT I'M PUZZLED, FLYBOY. YOU DON'T LOOK LIKE THE TYPE WHO SMOKES CIGARS.

WELL, I AM, HONEY.

by Cal App

by Milton Knish

END

HOW NOW CHARRED

BACKYARD

Barbecues come in assorted sizes and shapes. Simplest of these is the bowl-type, or *brazier*, with a grid top, mounted on tripod legs. This type is perfect for families with very limited backyard space.

COW DEPT.

HE DOESN'T MEAN OUT TO A FANCY RESTAURANT!
HE MEANS HE'S TAKING HER **OUTSIDE**, TO THE . . .

BARBECUE

Then there is the portable type of barbecue, mounted on wheels. This type affords convenience and mobility to the barbecue chef, and also comes in handy for chasing and pinning any guest who seems reluctant.

And then there's the super-type of barbecue, which is actually a converted blast-furnace. This explains why most outdoor chefs turn out hamburgers that are heavy as lead.

STARTING FIRE

The inexperienced chef lights his barbecue fire the hard way. First, he laboriously covers his charcoal with bits

The connoisseur of backyard barbecues lights his fire the easy way. First, he douses his charcoal with a specially

of paper and twigs, and then he touches his match to it.
The fire fizzles out before charcoal-broiling can begin. ▶

made inflammable fluid, and then touches his match to it.
The charcoal-broiled-meat aroma can be smelled for miles.

TESTING WIND DIRECTION

Always test the wind direction before you start the fire. Smoke may blow into house, forcing you to move barbecue.

Disadvantage of brick barbecue is now obvious. Smoke may blow into neighbor's house, forcing you to move family.

MAKING SHESHKABOB

This popular barbecue recipe is made by alternately impaling choice pieces of meat and vegetables on a long spit,

then revolving slowly over the **coals**. This is what is known as "done to a turn". The true outdoor chef, however,

uses genuine cavalry sword instead of spit. That way, if anybody refuses to eat the mess, he can run him through.

TOSSING SALAD

Place lettuce, tomatoes, raw carrots,
cucumbers and salad oil in neat pile.

For that extra kick, add a pineapple.

Barbecue salad will be nicely tossed.

BROILING STEAK

Steaks should be broiled to individual
tastes. Some people like them rare . . .

Some people like
them medium rare.

Some people like
them well - done.

But most people will get
them burned to a crisp!

FUTURE OUTDOOR LIVING

Backyard barbecues have become so popular, architects who design our future homes are planning to eliminate kitchens altogether. In fact, the more extreme elements among them are predicting a return to the primitive cave-like dwell-ing. They figure, if people are going to insist upon eat-ing like cave men, then they might as well *live* like them.

END

AND SO, ONE PREPOSTEROUS ARTICLE FOLLOWS ANOTHER. EVER DEDICATED TO THE CAUSE OF WIDENING AND IMPROVING ITS SCOPE OF READERS' INTERESTS,

MAD BUBBLE

You know how all those bubble-gum cards you ever collected up to now have been nothing but portraits of famous national figures, past and present, like for instance famous baseball heroes or famous war heroes or famous western heroes. You know how after a while you get sick and tired of famous heroes. Day after day, gum-wad after

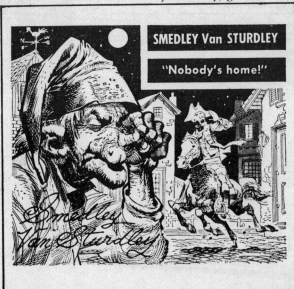

SMEDLEY Van STURDLEY

"Nobody's home!"

MAD NOW OFFERS HOBBYISTS AMONG YOU A RARE OPPORTUNITY. BE THE FIRST IN YOUR NEIGHBORHOOD TO BEGIN THIS EXCITING AND UNUSUAL COLLECTION OF ...

GUM CARDS

gum-wad, the same old famous heroes. Well, dear readers, here's your chance to get out of the rut. Here's your chance to throw away that dull old collection of corny bubble-gum cards featuring world famous heroes. Here's your chance to begin a dull *new* collection ... with this MAD starter-set of corny bubble-gum cards featuring world famous clods.

MAD GUM

SMEDLEY Van STURDLEY

Born: December 5, 1748
Height: 4'—3"
Weight: 109

Oaf
Concord, Mass.

When Paul Revere made his famous ride from Lexington to Concord, arousing the colonists at every Middlesex village and farm and warning them that the British were coming, it was Smedley Van Sturdley who **turned over and went back to sleep!**

FAMOUS COWARDS No. 1

©M.B.G.

Printed in U.S.A.

MILTON FORBISHER

"I lost my head!"

MAD GUM 2

MILTON FORBISHER

Born: October 9, 1752
Height: 7'—7"
Weight: 109

Minute Man
Boston, Mass.

At the battle of Bunker Hill, when that handful of Minute Men made their valient stand against an overwhelming force of red-coated British regulars, it was Milton Forbisher who panicked and shot before he saw the whites of their eyes!

FAMOUS COWARDS No. 2

©M.B.G.

Printed in U.S.A.

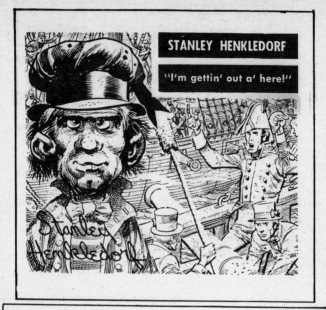

STANLEY HENKLEDORF

"I'm gettin' out a' here!"

MAD GUM 3

STANLEY HENKLEDORF
Born: July 3, 1788
Height: 5'—8"
Weight: 109

Poltroon
Getzville, N. Y.

During the war of 1812, at the famous naval battle of Lake Erie, when Commodore Perry, in the thick of the fight uttered those immortal words, it was Stanley Henkledorf who heedlessly turned, took to a long boat, and **did give up the ship!**

FAMOUS COWARDS   No. 3

©M.B.G.

Printed in U.S.A.

WALTER N. GOOBER

"I forget!"

MAD GUM 4

WALTER N. GOOBER

Born: August 7, 1808
Height: 6'
Weight: 109

Malingerer
Pecan Gap, Tex.

In the war of independence between Texas and Mexico, after General Santa Anna and four thousand Mexicans besieged and massacred Colonel William B. Travis and his gallant band of one hundred and eighty men, it was Walter N. Goober who **refused to remember the Alamo!**

FAMOUS COWARDS   No. 4

©M.B.G.

Printed in U.S.A.

BEAUREGARD BORDON

"Mooooooo-Hah!"

MAD GUM 5

BEAUREGARD BORDON

Bovine
Manassas Va.

Born: September 14, 1859
Weight: 1090

In the first pitched battle of the Civil War, General Johnston's Confederate forces opened fire on General Mc-Dowell's Union forces at Sudley's farm in Manassas, Virginia. Beauregard Bordon was caught in the middle, hence the name of this battle . . . boy, you should have seen that **bull run!**

FAMOUS COWARDS No. 5

©M.B.G.

Printed in I.N.K.

Just so people won't get the idea that MAD is a magazine strictly for clods, we've decided to get a little arty . . . and illustrate a famous poem. Here, then, for all you arty clods, is Don Martin's interpretation of . . .

THE
CHILDREN'S HOUR

By Henry Wadsworth Longfellow

Between the dark and the daylight,
When the night is beginning to lower,
Comes a pause in the day's occupations,
That is known as the Children's Hour.

2

I hear in the chamber above me
The patter of little feet,
The sound of a door that is opened,
And voices soft and sweet.

3

From my study I see in the lamplight,
Descending the broad hall stair,
Grave Alice, and laughing Allegra,
And Edith with golden hair.

4

A whisper, and then a silence:
  Yet I know by their merry eyes
They are plotting and planning together
  To take me by surprise.

5

A sudden rush from the stairway,
  A sudden raid from the hall!
By three doors left unguarded
  They enter my castle wall!

6

They climb up into my turret
   O'er the arms and back of my chair;
If I try to escape, they surround me;
   They seem to be everywhere.

7

They almost devour me with kisses,
   Their arms about me entwine,
Till I think of the Bishop of Bingen
   In his Mouse-Tower on the Rhine!

Do you think, O blue-eyed banditti,
  Because you have scaled the wall,
Such an old mustache as I am
  Is not a match for you all!

I have you fast in my fortress,
  And will not let you depart,
But put you down into the dungeon
  In the round-tower of my heart

10

And there will I keep you forever,
Yes, forever and a day,
Till the walls shall crumble to ruin,
And moulder in dust away!

11

END

DATING DEPT.

Since you are obviously a failure in the dating department, (You wouldn't be wasting time reading this trash if you could be going

THE

DATING

Up to now, you have probably approached the problem of dealing with the fair sex in one of two ways. You've either been the "shy" type, and you've failed miserably, or you've been the "aggressive" type, and you've failed miserably. Now, MAD shows you how to be the "Mad" type, and

THE SHY TYPE

THE AGGRESSIVE TYPE

out with girls!) MAD now offers you a rare opportunity to overcome your difficulties with this article which explains . . .

MAD

TECHNIQUE

fail miserably. All kidding aside though, let's go through a typical date, and see how these three types would handle the very same situations. When you've finished, it will be obvious to you that you've made many bad mistakes in your time, including starting this article in the first place.

THE MAD TYPE

ASKING FOR THE DATE

THE SHY TYPE hasn't enough nerve to ask for date, writes note instead, pays kid to deliver it. Unfortunately, girl usually accepts, goes out with the kid.

THE AGRESSIVE TYPE has plenty of nerve, asks girl for date right out. Unfortunately the girl also has plenty of nerve and she usually refuses outright.

THE MAD TYPE doesn't bother to ask, shows up at the girl's house with flowers, asks if she's ready. She hasn't enough nerve to admit she forgot date.

THE SHY TYPE hasn't the nerve to ask for his old man's car, so he rents one.

THE AGGRESSIVE TYPE doesn't even ask for his old man's car, he just steals it

THE MAD TYPE not only borrows old man's car, he also borrows the old man.

IMPRESSING THE GIRL'S FATHER

CHALLENGED BY DATE'S FATHER to Indian wrestle, the shy type purposely loses match, impresses father as a clod.

CHALLENGED BY DATE'S FATHER Indian wrestle, the aggressive typ throws father, impresses him as a clo

CHALLENGED BY DATE'S FATHER to
Indian wrestle, the MAD type throws
mother, impresses father as great guy.

IMPRESSING THE GIRL FINANCIALLY

THE SHY TYPE impresses his date by inadvertently leaving a big tip. He's too chicken to ask the waiter for change.

THE AGGRESSIVE TYPE impresses his date by impulsively leaving big tip. He eats candy-bar lunches all that week.

THE MAD TYPE impresses his date by deliberately leaving a big tip. He clever-ly swipes it all back as he leaves table.

LOOKING FOR A LITTLE PRIVACY

THE SHY TYPE stops car, pulls old routine about being out of gas. Date gets mad, so he ends up walking down dark lonely road to distant service station.

THE AGGRESSIVE TYPE stops car, pull out-of-gas' routine. Date gets mad, h gets mad, so she ends up walking dow lonely dark road to a distant bus stop

THE MAD TYPE doesn't resort to any corny routines. He crashes the car into a tree, and they *both* end up walking down that dark lonely road. Hoo-hah!

END

HOLLYWOOD DEPT. 2:

ANOTHER SCENE WE'D LIKE TO SEE

Escaping the Cannibals

END

Continuing its campaign of examining and extolling man's progress in his many fields of endeavor, MAD now turns its attention to the world of science, specifically to the complex art of modern photography, and in this next factual article (watch what happens when you turn the page) analyzes reasons

WHY

the precision engineered, highly perfected...

35 mm Camera

STACK OF RARE COINS
VIEW FINDER
FINDER FINDER
SHIRT BUTTON
CAMERA BUG
LENS BUTTON
EXHAUST
GENUINE LEATHER
ON SWITCH
OFF SWITCH
LENS SHADE
ROULETTE WHEEL

ESCAPE HATCH
WINDER
SIDE WINDER
REWIND WINDER
RANGE-FINDER WINDER
RANGE-FINDER FINDER
RANGE (ELECTRIC)
LIGHT METER
CHANNEL SELECTOR
ELECTRIC METER
METER METER
DRAIN PLUG

REPLACED

HANDLE

TOP PORT

BOTTOM PORT

BOTLED PORT

LENS

SAFETY PIN

SCOTCH TAPE

GENUINE IMITATION
LEATHERETTE

HINGE

TOP WINDER

TOP FINDER

SIDE FINDER

BOTTOM WINDER

SIDE WINDER

SHUTTER LEVER

the simple, unpretentious, primitive

Box Camera

MODERN 35mm CAMERA MAKES IT EASY TO GET FINE DETAIL AND HIGH-SPEED ACTION SHOTS NEVER BEFORE POSSIBLE

USING OUTMODED box camera, MAD's Seymour Fudd took this picture of a farmer and his children seated in a pasture. Note stiff, posed attitudes of subjects, lack of action, and blurred head of bull grazing contentedly in background. Nervous bull moved slightly while picture was being taken.

USING MODERN 35 mm camera, MAD's Wally Balloo caught this exciting shot of the same farmer and his children. Note how movement is stopped, showing subjects in midst of wild scramble. Nervous bull, grazing in background, suddenly charged wildly, enraged by Balloo's popping flashbulbs.

ABOVE PICTURE, taken by photographer Fudd, is another example of failing of undeveloped box camera. Due to fixed-focus lens, close-up shots are impossible, and all Fudd could get were dull shots like this one of a Bikini-clad model.

HOWEVER, with perfected 35 mm camera, plus portrait attachment, photographer Balloo was able to move in, capture amazing close-up-detail shots just like startling picture above of the same Bikini-clad model.—Interesting, huh?

Now let's compare quality of the box

Study actual-size contact print (above) made from film shot with old-fashioned box camera. Note that images in picture are strangely fuzzy, gray, and lacking in definition. Now compare to actual-size contact print (right), made from film shot with modern 35mm camera. Note that images in picture are sharp, clear, well-contrasted, and mainly impossible to see with the naked eye. However, this one drawback can be quickly remedied. With the use of expensive equipment, enlargement (upper right) can be produced, equal in size to box camera print, with images that are strangely fuzzy, gray, and lacking in definition.

Wally Balloo, MAD photographer, with equipment used in conjunction with 35mm Camera

(a) Ever-ready camera case. (b) Tripod. (c) Flash gun.
(d) Flash bulbs. (e) Exposure meter. (f) Lens cap.
(g) Filters.   (h) Filter adapters.   (i) Strobe light
(j) Power pack for strobe light.   (k) Enlarger.

TOTAL COST: $1326.45

IN THIS ARTICLE WE HAVE EXAMINED AND

EVALUATED REASONS THE 35mm CAMERA

Seymour Fudd, MAD photographer, with equipment used in conjunction with Box Camera

a) Film.   (b) Sun.

OTAL COST: 45¢

REPLACED THE BOX CAMERA. NOW FOR US, JUST ONE QUESTION REMAINS UNAN-SWERED: *WHY?*

END

ONCE UPON A TIME DEPT.

These days, fairy tales are big business. Take the story of Cinderella, the little girl with the weird taste in shoes. First, Walt Disney made millions on his animated version. Next, Leslie Caron danced her psychiatric way to a box-office bonanza. Then Rogers and Hammerstein guaranteed their old age security with a TV spectacular composed of leftover

SIN-DOLL

Tennessee

ACT I, SCENE 1: Curtain rises on disgustin' decayin' bedroom of disgustin' decayin' shack in disgustin' decayin' South. Heroine, Ella, sleeps in southern comfort with a tunes from South Pacific. And recently, the Saddler's Wells Company cashed in on their ballet interpretation. So who are we to fight a trend? Here, then, in an effort to make a quick buck, is our brand new version of that over-worked fairy tale, Cinderella, written especially for MAD by a world-famous, ultra-sophisticated Broadway playwright ...

ELLA
by
Williamsburg

bottle (or is it with a bottle of Southern Comfort?). MUSIC: A few disgustin' decayin' bars of Eli Whitney's "Get Yore Cotton' Pickin' Hands Off Mah Gin"...

ACT I, SCENE II: Light gradually to give effect o
summer evening. There's an aroma of magnolias, th
hum of insects, the singin' of birds, an' the sound
of a barnyard chorus, all emergin' from orchestra pi

SPECIAL EFFECT: Fairy Godmother appears in a puff of smoke. If stringent state censorship prevails, clothes can easily be substituted for puff of smoke.

Mama mia! Whata stinkin' mess! What's-a-matta, **you** feed-a-de pigs when everyone **else,** she's-a havin' a ball? Hah?

ACT II: The Ball. Colored lights fill room as Southern damsels blush behind fans. Nearby, Confederate soldiers converse profanely. That's why Southern damsels blush behind fans. Big Fat Daddy eyes damsels. His son, Prince Kowalski, eyes Confederate Soldiers. Ella enters ballroom, followed by Fairy Godmother . . .

Ah shore hopes tonight's assortment of delectable damsels will inspire yo into takin' a wife, m'boy. Ah see that gal who jus' entered has caught yo eye. Is yo starin' at her lovely face, or her lovely figger?

126

Time for the commercial, gang...so here we go with another sample Story Board of...

FUTURE
TV. ADS

2

3

5 Whaddya gonna do? Sleep all day? Gonna lose your new job like ya' did the last eight? Honestly, George, what's wrong with you lately? George?

133

14

15

END

138

SCIENCE DEPT.

When Milwaukee's Donald Knuth first presented his revolutionary system of weights and measures to the members of the *Wisconsin Academy of Science, Arts, and Letters*, they were astounded...mainly because Donald also has two heads. All kidding aside, Donald's system won first prize as the "most original presentation". So far, the system has been adopted in Tierra del Fuego, Afghanistan, and Southern Rhodesia. The U.N. is considering it for world adoption.

THE POTRZEBIE SYSTEM
OF WEIGHTS
AND MEASURES

This new system of measuring, which is destined to become the measuring system of the future, has decided improvements over the other systems now in use. It is based upon measurements taken 6-9-12 at the Physics Lab. of Milwaukee Lutheran High School, in Milwaukee, Wis., when the thickness of MAD Magazine #26 was determined to be 2.26334851-7438173216473 mm. This length is the basis for the entire system, and is called one potrzebie of length.

The Potrzebie has also been standardized at 3515.-3502 wave lengths of the red line in the spectrum of cadmium. A partial table of the Potrzebie System, the measuring system of the future, is given.

LENGTH

1 potrzebie = thickness of MAD #26
.000001 p = 1 farshimmelt potrzebie (fp)
1000 fp = 1 millipotrzebie (mp)
10 mp = 1 centipotrzebie (cp)
10 cp = 1 decipotrzebie (dp)

VOLUME

1 cubic dekapotrzebie = 1 ngogn (n)
.000001 n = 1 farshimmelt ngogn (fn)
1000 fn = 1 millingogn (mn)
10 mn = 1 centingogn (cn)
10 cn = 1 decingogn (dn)

MASS

1 ngogn of halavah* = 1 blintz (b)
.000001 b = 1 farshimmelt blintz (b)
1000 fb = 1 milliblintz (mb)
10 mb = 1 centiblintz (c)
10 cb = 1 deciblintz (db)

*Halavah is a form of pie,
3.1416 and a specific heat.

10 dp = 1 potrzebie (p)
10 p = 1 dekapotrzebie (Dp)
10 Dp = 1 hectopotrzebie (Hp)
10 Hp = 1 kilopotrzebie (Kp)
1000 Kp = 1 furshlugginer potrzebie (Fp)

10 dn = 1 ngogn (n)
10 n = 1 dekangogn (Dn)
10 Dn = 1 hectongogn (Hn)
10 Hn — 1 kilongogn (Kn)
1000 Kn = 1 furshlugginer ngogn (Fn)

10 db = 1 blintz (b)
10 b = 1 dekablintz (Db)
10 Db = 1 hectoblintz (Hb)
10 Hb = 1 kiloblintz (Kb)
1000 Kb = 1 furshlugginer blintz (Fb)

and it has a specific gravity of
of .31416.

TIME

1 average rotation of the earth = 1 clarke (cl)

.00001 cl = 1 wolverton (wl)

1000 wl = 1 kovac (kv)

100 kov = 1 martin (mn)

100 mn = 1 wood (wd)

10 wd = 1 clarke (cl)

10 cl = 1 mingo (mi)

10 mi = 1 cowznofski (cow)

DATE

October 1, 1952 is the day MAD was first published according to the old calendar. On new calendar, this is price 1 of cowznofski 1. Cowznofskis before this date are referred to as "Before MAD (B.M.)" and cowznofskis following this date are referred to as "Cowznofsko Madi (C.M.)" The calendar for each cowznofski contains 10 mingos named as follows: 1. Tales (Tal.) 2. Calculated (Cal.) 3. To (To) 4. Drive (Dri.) 5. You (You) 6. Humor (Hum.) 7. In (In) 8. A (A) 9. Jugular (Jug.) 10. Vein (Vei.)

FORCE (absolute)

a force which, when acting upon 1 blintz of mass for 1 kovac, causes it to attain a velocity of 1 potrzebie per kovac = 1 blintzal (b-al).
1000000 b-al = 1 furshlugginer blintzal (Fb-ál)

ENERGY AND WORK

1 blintzal-potrzebie = 1 hoo (h)
1000000 h = 1 hah (hh)

POWER

1 hah per kovac = 1 whatmeworry (WMW)
1000 WMW = 1 kilowhatmeworry (KWMW).
100 KWMW = 1 aeolipower (A.P.)

RADIOACTIVITY

The quantity of radon which is in equilibrium with one blintz of radium = 1 hyme (how's your mom, ed)

HEAT ENERGY

The amount of heat necessary to raise one blintz of hala-vah 1° S = 1 vreeble (v.) 1000 v = 1 large vreeble (V)

THIS END UP

TEMPERATURE

100° Smurdley (S) = optimum temperature
for eating halavah (27°C.)

COUNTING

48 things = 1 MAD
49 things = 1 baker's MAD

ANGULAR MEASURE

100 quircits (''') = 1 zorch ('')
100 zorch ('') = 1 zygo (§)
100 zygo (§) = 1 circle or circumference

BASIC CONVERSION

1 inch = 11.222 potrzebie
·1 mile = .71105 Fur-potrzebie
1 blintz = 36.42538631 grams
1 kiloblintz = 80.3048 pounds
1 Fur-blintz = 36.425 metric tons
1 ngogn = 11.59455 cc = .0125 qts.
     = 2.3523 teaspoons

MISCELLANEOUS MEASUREMENTS

1 light Cowz. $= 1.14 \times 10^{12}$ Fp.
1 vreeble $= 574.8$ hah
1 cosmo per sq. potrzebie $= 3.1416$ bumbles.
1 faraday $= 122300$ blobs/blintz equivalent weight.
1 electron-ech $= 5.5794 \times 10^{15}$ hoo
1 blintz molecular wt. of a gas $= 77.4$ Cn

Density of $H_2O = .31823$ blintzes per ngogn (distilled water).

1 atmosphere pressure $= 1.4532 \dfrac{b^2}{p}$
335.79 p of Hg.

1 b $= 3234.4$ b-al
gravity $= 3234.4$ p per kov. per kov.
speed of light $= 114440$ Fp/Kov.

FACTORS (ABBREVIATED TABLE)

1 potrzebie $= 2.2633$ millimeters
.089106 inches
1 Furshlugginer potrzebie $=$
2.2633 Klm.
1.4064 miles
1 centimeter $= 4.4182$ potrzebie
1 kilometer $= .44182$ Fur-potrzebie

1 wood $= 144$ minutes
1 kovac $= .864$ seconds
1 year $= 3.6524$ Cowznofskis
1 watt $= 3.499651$ Whatmeworries
1 Horse Power $= 2.57$ Kilowhatmeworry
1 Aeolipower $= 38.797$ Horse Power.
1 vreeble $= 34.330$ calories

E N D

DEAD

Since we don't make enough money to live on when we write this trash, we recently took a night job spinning cobwebs in the "Dead Letter" section of New York's Main Post Office. Seeing all those undelivered letters caused us to speculate . . . might not the world be a lot different today if they had reached the people for whom they were intended? So we opened a random few to prove our point. Another point we prove is—you can get arrested tampering with U. S. Mail!

LETTERS

John T. Stuart
Attorney-At-Law
Springfield, Illinois

April 3rd, 1865

A. Lincoln
The White House
Washington, D.C.

Dear Abe:-

Saw "Our American Cousin"
when it played Chicago.
It's a bomb! Do yourself
a favor. Stay home!

- John

Office of the Field Secretary
THE SALVATION ARMY
Hollywood, California

Sept. 24, 1948

Miss Marylin Monroe
% Schwabs Drug Store
Hollywood and Vine
Hollywood, California

Dear Miss Monroe:-

Your application to join the Salvation
Army has been approved by this office.
Kindly report to our School for Officers
Training in San Francisco, on October 9th,
1948, at 10 A.M.

Bless you,

Emilia Dermquod

Emilia Dermquod
Brigadier

THE MILLS HOTEL

Transient and Resident Accommodations for Single Men.

May 19, 1927

Charles A. Lindbergh
Roosevelt Field
Mineola, L. I.

Mon cher Charles,
    Am unavoidably delayed.
Will not make scheduled
take-off time. Wait for me!

    You cannot find Paris
without me.

            Your co-pilot,
            Gaspard,

July 22, 1886

Miss Tillie Monohan
242 Flatbush Avenue
Brooklyn, N.Y.

Dearest Tillie,
   My heart is ~~bor~~ broke
because you have refused
my proposal of marriage.
   I will be on the Brooklyn
Bridge tomorrow at 4 P.M.
Meet me there and tell
me you have changed your
mind.
   Otherwise I will kill
myself!!
                No kiddin!
                Steve Brodie

COOK COUNTY BOARD of HEALTH
Chicago, Illinois

October 1, 1871

Mrs. Gertrude O'Leary
Cor. Jefferson & DeKoven Sts.
Chicago, Illinois

Dear Mrs. O'Leary:-

It has been brought to our attention by complaints from your neighbors, that you are harboring a live cow in a residential area of Chicago proper, contrary to Provision 189, Section 4, Cook County Health Code.

Please be advised that if you do not remove said cow from your area by October 8, 1871, you will be subject to a fine in the amount of $2.00.

Respectfully yours,

Melvin J. Finnigan

Melvin J. Finnigan
Commissioner of Health

Cuartel General de la Marina

REAL ARSENAL NAVAL
LA HABANA, CUBA

January 20, 1898

TO: Captain Charles D. Sigsbee, USN, Commanding
U.S.S. Battleship MAINE
Naval Station
Key West, Florida, U.S.A.

FROM: Capitán de Navío Edelmiro Gonzales
Commandant of Port Facilities,
Havana, Cuba.

Dear Captain Sigsbee:-

It is with pleasure that we learn of your impen-
ding good-will visit to our fair city on the mag-
nificent American Battleship MAINE. Please be advised that our Corps of Engineers will be carrying
on blasting operations for the purpose of deepen-
ing Havana harbor, so may I respectfully suggest
that when you arrive, you anchor safely outside
of the harbor limits.

Cordially yours,

Edelmiro Gonzales

Capitán de Navío
Royal Spanish Navy

152

U. S. MALE DEPT.

These days, men aren't "men" unless they read "men's" magazines. And "men's" magazines aren't for "men" unless they're full of "he-men" type articles. So MAD wouldn't be "mad" if it didn't poke some fun at "men's" magazines like:

RAW GUTS

THE MAGAZINE FOR HE-MEN

DEC. 1957   TWO BITS

THE BLOODY MESS ON
THE FLOOR WAS ME

I LOST AT
RUSSIAN ROULETTE
AND LIVED!

ARTICLES

I Had A Rendezvous With Death
(But Didn't Show Up)

I TALKED BACK TO MY WIFE

It Only Hurts When I Snarl

HOW TO GET THE SCAR THAT
FITS YOUR PERSONALITY

What To Say When You
Meet A Gorilla

HARI KARI MADE EASY

Converting the
M-1 Sub Machine Gun
To Sporting Use

. . . and many more
Guts-type articles

The Men Who Bea

t The AMAZON!

by Mickey Cohen

MVMBA, our guide, staggered into camp with the news. Up ahead, a giant Armadillo was pinching female members of the Itchigoochi. The Itchigoochi were friendly. We couldn't let them down! Only the river stood between us. The mighty Amazon River. We had to cross it. But how? It was too late to rent a canoe. There was only one answer.

Sturdley was the first to hit the water. One after the other, we all followed suit, hitting the water. It was a most grotesque spectacle. Imagine! Grown-up men hitting and punching innocent water! CONTINUED

Illustrations by Matt Tisse7

I CAPTURED SIX JAPS WITH ONE HAND!

by Lt. Col. William "Willie" Sutton

It was the most terrifying experience of my life. Just think of it. Six one-handed Japs. How they were ever taken into the Japanese Army, I'll never know. And I didn't wait to find out. When they came marching toward me, each with his one hand raised in surrender, I took off for H. Q. They had quite a job keeping up with me, as

CONTINUED

Illustrations by Leo Nardo

I Fought A
GRIZZLY BEAR
BLINDFOLDED!

by Al Anastasia

How a big old grizzly like that ever managed to get himself blindfolded is beyond me. But he sure looked funny as he charged. I couldn't help but laugh in his face as his huge paws closed around me in a crushing embrace, he looked that funny.

Even now, as I look back on it, lying here in the hospital room, I have to laugh. Only I can't because it hurts

CONTINUED

Illustrations by Mike L. Angelo

I Warned The Warden That I Would BREAK OUT!

by Johnny Dio

The fool didn't believe me. So I showed him, the next day. It was the worst break-out he'd ever seen at Leavenworth. My whole body was covered with these big, ugly purple blotches. The doctor had warned me about my allergy to Lasagna and Chicken Fat. And there it was on my mess tray, the very first meal.

CONTINUED

Illustrations by
Sal Vadordall

I FOUGHT

With The Boys Of The

26 th INFANTRY

by Maj. Gen. Frank Costello

Yes! I fought with the boys of the 26th Infantry! I also fought with the boys of the 39th Infantry! Then I fought with the boys of the 47th Infantry! It seems that I just couldn't get along with anybody while I was in the army.

I remember as a child that I used to fight with all the kids on my block

CONTINUED

I CLEANED UP AN
ENEMY OUTPOST
BARE-HANDED!

by Sgt. John Dillinger D.O.A.

Lucky for me, there was nobody there at the time. Nevertheless, it was a risky proposition . . . cleaning it up barehanded. They didn't even give me a decent broom.

One thing I can say about being a P. W., the German policy on treatment

CONTINUED

Illustrations by P. Casso

HE WAS AN OLD LION KILLER!

by Lucky Luciano

The only trouble was, there just weren't any more old lions around to kill. And the young ones were much too ferocious for him.

He had to find some other way to release his deep-rooted hostilities.

And so, that's how Fenwick Furd started molesting young innocent

CONTINUED

Illustrations by Della Croix

END

Science, in its never-ending march of progress, dedicated to improving man's lot on Earth (or blowing the place up in the attempt!), has somehow neglected one of the most important functions of life. Eating! When it comes to the dining room table, we're still in the Middle Ages. Those

MAD

UTEN

nives, forks, and spoons we use today to spill stuff **on** ur best ties are basically the same as the ones the Ro- nans used to spill stuff on their best togas. Nobody ever othered to redesign them and bring them up to date. No- ody, that is, until now. Now, *we* try ... and fail ... with

EATING

SILS

While careful grafting and cross-pollinating has eliminated most of the seeds from the popular grapefruit, no one has been able, as yet, to eliminate its squirt. Scenes like one at left can be eliminated once and for all with MAD's

**SQUIRTPROOF
SELF-WIPING
GRAPEFRUIT SPOON**

Before the beer foams up and cascades down the sides of the glass all over your hand, one thing to do is blow it off, as fellow in scene at left is doing. But if you're sick of the bartender punching you in the eye, use MAD's

**FOAM-CATCHING
BEER GLASS**

166

If you've ever struggled with spaghetti, you know what torture fellow on left is going through. No matter how much you wind and wind, you still end up with strands of the stuff dangling down your chin. So stop buying new ties. Use MAD's

NO-HANG
SPAGHETTI FORK

There's nothing quite as frustrating as that last drop of delicious soup or fruit-cup juice you just can't scoop up unless you break every rule of etiquette and tilt the dish. Now you can suck it all up with the straw built into MAD's

LAST DROP
SOUP AND FRUIT CUP
SPOON

Here's another familiar problem: how do you keep those elusive little devils, carrots and peas, from rolling off your fork and sloshing gravy on your brand new sport shirt like guy on left is doing? The answer is simple: just use MAD's

CARROTS AND PEAS SPEARER

If you are like Susan, the lazy housewife on the left, you are sick and tired of that pile of dinner dishes every night. And who can blame you? But have you ever asked yourself if dishes are really necessary when you can use MAD's

LAZY-SUSAN DISH-SAVER

If you're a mixed-drink man, and you've had it as far as choking on all those ice cubes you accidentally swallow, or as far as watered-down highballs are concerned, then you'll hail MAD's

NO-DILUTING ANTI-CHOKE DRINK GLASS

Invariably, when you're invited out to someone's house for dinner, they serve steak. And invariably it's tough. When you try cutting it with an ordinary knife, what happens is pictured at left. Beat this problem by bringing your MAD

TOUGH MEAT BUZZ-SAW KNIFE

If you're a tea drinker, or you switched recently because you like Arthur Godfrey (there are such people!), then you know how, when you wring out the teabag so it won't drip on the tablecloth, it drips on the fingers. Well, not with MAD's

TEA BAG SQUEEZER

Take a nice fresh slice of white bread, and try buttering it with cold hard butter. You know what happens. The same thing that's happening to the guy on the left. Total destruction. But it won't happen if you use MAD's self-heated

COLD BUTTER SPREADER

A baffling problem that plagues the Martini set is: how to fish out the olive, cherry, or onion once the drink's gone. Spearing it with finger-nail is frowned on. The only solution is MAD's

COMBINATION COCKTAIL-STIRRER CHERRY-NETTER

Slob on left has just finished cool glass of milk. Note tell-tale white moustache on top lip. If this happens to you, you too are a slob. Remain a slob and still enjoy cool glass of milk without that tell-tale moustache. Use a MAD

NO-MOUSTACHE MILK GLASS

Ever try to butter hot corn-on-the-cob? Ever try to hold it and eat it after you finally do get it buttered? If you have, then you'll surely appreciate the new MAD

SELF-BUTTERING NO-TOUCH CORN-ON-THE-COB HOLDER

Biggest problem facing the American people is: how does one watch TV and eat dinner at same time without having to look down to see what to scoop up next, thereby missing what happens on screen? Answer: shovel food direct from MAD's

NO-LOOK-DOWN TV TRAY
END

END

Leave us face it . . .

. . . this is a heck of a

Uncivilized, isn't it? And yet, in the homes they share all over the country, millions of innocent American mice are daily meeting this same sudden cruel fate. Think about this for a moment or two. Think hard about this. Think of *yourself* in this mouse's shoes. By George, you'll *have* to think hard about this, since any fool knows mice don't wear shoes!

MAD BUILDS A

MOUSE

thing to do to a mouse!

All kidding aside, this article has been written because MAD has a conscience. This article has been written because MAD has a feeling for poor little animals. But mainly, this article has been written because MAD has these eight pages to fill up. And so, on these eight pages, MAD suggests six new approaches to the problem of trapping mice. On these eight pages . . .

MORE CIVILIZED
TRAP

Culture-loving mouse passes through attractive entrance (A) of trap designed to look like high class art gallery (B). Corridors (C) and (D) are lined with framed microscopic reproductions of valuable old masters. Door to salon (E) has sign (F) announcing special showing of original world famous painting of the Mona Lisa. Excited mouse rushes into salon (G), sees frame (H) with canvas (I) slashed to ribbons (J), and has heart attack.

Muscle-flexing, he-man-type mouse is urged by cleverly-worded sign (A) to prove strength by slamming lever (B) with sledge-hammer (C) sending weight (D) up wire (E) ringing bell on top (F). Gullible mouse confidently makes attempt (G) but ingeniously tapered wire (E) prevents weight (D) from reaching bell (F). Stubborn mouse, after trying in vain all night, collapses from exhaustion.

Science-Fiction-minded mouse, lured from hole (A) by strange recorded sound (B), watches in awe as mechanical flying saucer (C) makes simulated landing. Mouse's excitement mounts as door in saucer (D) opens and ladder (E) is extended. At sight of emerging horrible alien creature (F), terrified mouse drops dead.

Civic-minded mouse sees marquee (A) announcing big mass-meeting political rally, eagerly enters doorway (B) of trap designed to look like huge auditorium jammed with stuffed mice (C), moves down aisle (D), slides into only available seat (E), turns attention to rabble-rousing mechanical speaker (F) delivering tape-recorded political address (G), and is scalded to death by blasts of hot air.

Reader-of-Mad-Type Mouse, attracted from hole (A) by current issue of this magazine (B) opened to this article (C), sees sheer idiocy of suggested civilized approaches (D, E, F, G, & H), knows that old-fashioned gadget is only effective method of trapping mice, and dies laughing.

Neurotic-type mouse impulsively enters door (A) of trap designed to look like mouse-psychiatrist's office (B), lies down on couch (C), tells all to mechanical nodding mouse-analyst (D) for usual hour session (E), is then handed bill (F), and at sight of outlandish charge (G), blows top.

END

The Railroad Timetable

At first glance a railroad timetable appears to be cluttered, unreadable and senseless. Actually, it is! Study this timetable of one of America's least-traveled lines, the Chicago, Lasagna & South Gasp Railroad. After you've finished, we here at MAD are certain you'll conclude the only way to travel is by car...

CHICAGO, LASAGNA & SOUTH GASP RAILROAD

ALL CATTLE CARS ARE AIR-CONDITIONED

For equipment needed to survive on these trains see p. 8

WESTBOUND (Read down—How else?)			21 Daily	7 Ex. Sun. ᴅ	11 Ex. Sat.	23 Daily	101 Weekly	5739 Monthly	65 Hardly
Miles			AM	AM	AM	AM	AM	PM	PM
0	CHICAGO	351 Lv.	1 06	2 14	6 11	6 12	6 13	3 56	5 31'
10	Ulcer	1577 Ar.		2 59	7 30			7 15	
215	E. Frammis	2344 "		5 16	9 14ᴾᴾ				10 30
215½	Frammis	4432 "		5 09	10 02ᵀ				
215	W. Frammis	2443 "		5 17	7 15	8 20z			
230	Neumanville	4567 "			10 45				
235	Fort Fungus, Iowa	5678 "			3 11	9 14			
240	Stump City	6 "			4 35				
245	Gopher Prairie	17 "			5 55				
260	Haggenfrans	2 "			5 56				
281	Undertow	-37 "			8 09				
300	Elbowgrease	-688 "			10 55		6 14		
319	Whoops, Missouri	1 "	3 11		1 03				
324	K-k-k-kankakee	? "	3 46½		1 31ǫ				
325	W. Crocus, Iowa	5 "	8 02		5 43				
326	Lake Pheugfth	10 "	11 51		7 00				
327	LASAGNA	15 "	1 05		7 17	12 35	8 30	6 15a	
370	Buzzardville	20 "	10 14		11 30		1 54		12 15ᵥᵥ
381	E. Asterisk, Arkansas	25 "			1 05ᴴ				
394	Munch	30 "			2 34ʰʰ				
402	Crunch	No! "	4 19		2 34ⁱⁱ		4 45ᵏᵏ		
411	Hopeless Crossing	101 "			9 30ᴷ			6 16ᴬᴬ	
901	Snerdsberg, Tennessee	6¾ "	5 03ʳʳ		9 56				4 45ᴄ
912	Toadstool	5¾ "			9 59				
934	Ft. Apache, Arizona	4001 "			*1 34	*4 45	*2 36ᵥ		
937	Bedspring ♪	88 "			1 56ᴘ				
944	Buckskin	888 "			ᴍ				
952	Riboflavin ᴺᴺ	8888 "	4 15						
963	New Molar, California	3481 "	6 17ʸ						
981	Fritter ᴑ	31 "	9 55						8 30
999	SOUTH GASP	0 "	10 30	10 30	·10 30	10 30	10 30		10 30

*Vertical train notes appearing through the columns:*
- THE AARDVAK ᶻᶻ Will not run Dec. 25, Jan. 1 or any other day, for that matter.
- THE CALVIN COOLIDGE ǂ Will not run even if nominated)
- THE SILK STOCKING ᵀ If caught, will run.
- THE ANARCHIST ǂ No baggage, no passengers, no engineer.
- THE MUDDER ᴿᴿ Will not run if track is fast.

EXPLANATION OF REFERENCE MARKS

a Does not stop on odd-numbered Thursdays.

ᴬᴬ Adjust oxygen masks.

ᴇ When the engineer feels like it.

ᴅ Not this Sunday.

ᵥ Does not carry passengers born in the month of May.

ᴴ Train whistle hits a perfect high "C" at this point.

ʰʰ Stops to let off paying passengers.

ᵏᵏ Stops to throw off non-paying passengers.

ᴊ Station Master noted for repertoire of snappy stories.

ᴊᴊ Rarely on time.

ᴷ Stops to throw Mama from the train a knish.

ˡˡ Last week.

ᴍ Tomorrow.

ᴹᴹ Sun rises at 7:09 a.m.

ᴑ Observation car carries spittoon once used by William Jennings Bryan.

ᴑ Nice looking blonde sells candy here.

ᴾᴾ Look, Ma! No hands!

ᴘ Avalanche!

ǫ See note "a."

ʳʳ Last call for dinner.

ᴺᴺ Conductor's middle name is Sidney.

ᵀ All seats on this train reserved in advance, otherwise you got to sit on your luggage.

ʀ Friendly pickpockets in club car.

ᵥᵥ Four-day layover.

ᵥ Alternate Mondays.

ˣˣ Don't order corned beef and cabbage in the diner unless you have supply of Bicarbonate of Soda along.

ʸ Bus leaves every hour for Jamaica, Post time: 3:45, Pari-Mutuels at the track.

z If you're lucky.

* Mountain time prevails in this territory, but trains are operated under Central Time. For equivalent Pacific Time, figure one hour earlier than Mountain Time and two hours earlier than Central Time if you got the time.

THE SEASIDE INCIDENT

END